MONSTER

ets a job

19

One day Monster and the little boy
finish a good breakfast.
Monster takes out this list—
PRESENTS FOR BIRTHDAYS.

The little boy goes and gets
the piggy bank. They are looking
very sad because they don't have
enough money to buy birthday presents
for their friends.

Monster could have borrowed some money
but he doesn't know anyone with
enough money. Then Monster says,
"I know what I'll do. I'll get a job."

2

He looks through the paper
until he comes to a page that says,
"HELP WANTED."
Monster says, "Here's a good job—
car mechanic. I've wanted to be
a car mechanic all my life.
You have to know a lot about cars,
how to repair them, how to put on
new silencers and new tyres.
You also get very dirty."

Monster goes to the garage. He wants
to get the job, but he doesn't know
what to do. He doesn't know
where the man is to talk to.

Monster is looking at the sign.
He should have looked under the car.
That's where the man is who is mending
the car. His feet are sticking out
from under the car.

Monster thinks there is nobody there
to talk to, so he leaves.
He leaves and goes home.

Monster goes home and looks in
the newspaper again. He sees
another job, a job for a taxi driver.
He says, "Perhaps I could be a taxi driver."
The little boy says, "Perhaps so."

Monster gets a job as a taxi driver
but he doesn't know how to drive
very well. He doesn't like
the horns hooting at him.

The people in the back of his taxi
are shouting at Monster. They say,
"Stop, stop! You're going too fast."

A van driver is shouting at Monster
because Monster is going too slow.
The van driver yells,
"Get out of the way!"

Monster feels nervous. He's getting
a headache. Everyone is hooting at him.
People are screaming at him.
Some people say he's going too slow.
Some people say he's going too fast.
There is a terrible noise.

Monster doesn't know what to do
in traffic. He doesn't know
how to be a very good taxi driver.
He's getting into a terrible mess.

Monster doesn't like that job at all
so he looks in the paper
one more time.

He looks at the adverts for dog walkers.
This job means that Monster
has to walk people's dogs every day.

There might be a problem with this job
because the dogs may not like him
and they may try to bite him or growl
at him. Monster says, "I may as well
try this."

Monster goes to the first house
and knocks on the door. He asks
the lady, "Do you want me
to walk your dog? I'm a dog walker."

The lady gives Monster a funny look.
She thinks he's awfully big.

The lady and her dog look the same.
Their noses are the same.
Their faces look the same.
But the dog has whiskers.

Monster gets the job. The lady tells
Monster that he can walk her dog.
She says, "Goodbye," to her dog.

Then Monster goes to another house.
He tells the man, "I am a dog walker.
I'm already walking this dog.
I can walk your dog too."

He will have to be careful.
The dogs might have a fight
or their leads might get mixed up.

The man has a pointed nose
and the dog has a pointed face.
Their hair looks alike.

The man says, "All right."
He gives his dog to Monster.
He lets Monster walk his dog.

Monster goes to another house.
Monster says, "Do you want me
to walk your dog?" The man says,
"That would be nice."

This man has two dogs. Now Monster has
four dogs to walk. There might be trouble.
If Monster makes a mess of it,
people won't let him walk their dogs
so he'll have to be careful.

Monster decides to take the dogs
to the park to play with them.

He plays ball with the dogs. All the dogs
jump and bark. They try to get the ball.
They're having such fun.

One of the dogs wants Monster
to rub his stomach.

22

But one of the dogs gets loose and
runs away. There's going to be trouble!
Monster has lost one of the dogs.

23

Monster runs all over the park trying
to find the lost dog. He's so anxious
to get the dog back. He asks
all the children if they have seen
the lost dog. The children say, "No."

Monster asks the policeman on a horse
if he has seen the dog.
The policeman says, "I see a lot
of dogs running around here."

Monster asks more people if they have
seen the dog. They all say, "No."
They haven't seen the dog.

Monster looks sad. He's worried.
If he goes back without the dog
he's going to get in trouble.
And he'll lose his job.

Monster is searching everywhere
that the dog might be. All of a sudden
Monster looks over at the pool
the children use.

There is the dog drinking water!

Monster is going to try and sneak over
to catch the dog while he's playing
in the water.

Monster is chasing after the dog.
He runs faster and faster.

When the dog hears Monster's footsteps
he starts running.
All the dogs start barking.

Then all of a sudden Monster
puts his foot down on the dog's lead.
The lost dog stops running. He looks funny
because Monster caught him
all of a sudden.

Monster and the dogs sit under a tree
to rest. Monster is tired and sweaty
from running. All the dogs are tired too
because they ran so much.
The dogs decide to stay with Monster
and not to run away. Now they are friendly.

They lie in Monster's lap
and they lick Monster all over.

Monster feels so good
because he got the dog back.
All the dogs are his friends now.
Monster is proud to be a dog walker.

Monster walks the dogs back to
their owners. The lady gives Monster money
for walking her dog, and so does the man.

Monster takes the other dogs back
and gets paid. The man says,
"Thank you for walking my dogs.
See you tomorrow."

Monster is happy. When he gets home
he shows the little boy how much money
he has. All the money is in his hand.
He can hold it all with one hand
because his hand is so big.

The little boy brings Monster
some tea and biscuits
because he knows Monster is tired.

Now Monster has enough money
to buy some presents and he has a job.
Isn't that nice?

Monster gets a job

What would children do if they needed money to buy presents for someone's birthday? Perhaps they would do what Monster did. What job would they like and what problems do they think they might encounter? How long do they think they would have to work to earn enough money to buy the things they want to buy? These are good questions for children to think about and to discuss.

Ann Cook
Ellen Blance